KU-044-002

Piano • Vocal • Guitar

IMPOSSIBLE
...PLUS 11 MORE TOP HITS

WISE PUBLICATIONS
part of The Music Sales Group
London / New York / Paris / Sydney / Copenhagen / Berlin / Madrid / Hong Kong / Tokyo

Published by
Wise Publications
14-15 Berners Street, London W1T 3LJ, UK.

Exclusive Distributors:

Music Sales Limited
Distribution Centre, Newmarket Road,
Bury St Edmunds, Suffolk IP33 3YB, UK.

Music Sales Pty Limited
Units 3-4, 17 Willfox Street, Condell Park,
NSW 2200, Australia.

Order No. AM1006291
ISBN: 978-1-78305-001-7
This book © Copyright 2013 Wise Publications,
a division of Music Sales Limited.

Edited by Jenni Norey.
Cover design by Tim Field.

Printed in the EU.

Beneath Your Beautiful

Words & Music by Timothy McKenzie, Mike Posner
& Emeli Sandé

I wan-na see___ in - side. Would you let me___ see be - neath___ your beau-ti - ful___ to-

-night?

2. You let all the girls_ go.___ Makes you feel good,_ don't it?

Be-hind your Broad-way show_____ I heard a voice_ say "Please_ don't_ hurt me."_

I wan-na see__ in-side. Would you let me__ see be-neath__ your beau-ti-ful__ to-

-night? *vocal ad lib.*

I'm gon-na climb on top your iv-'ry__ tow-er. I'll hold your hand and then we'll

Candy

Words & Music by Robbie Williams, Gary Barlow
& Terje Olsen

1. I was there to wit - ness_ Can - dice - 's in - ner bus - 'ness._ She
2. Ring a ring of ro - ses_ who - ev - er gets the clo - sest._ She

wants the boys to no - tice_ her rain - bows and her po - nies. She was ed - u - ca - ted_ but
comes and she goes as_ the war of_ the ro - ses._ Moth - er was a vic - tim._

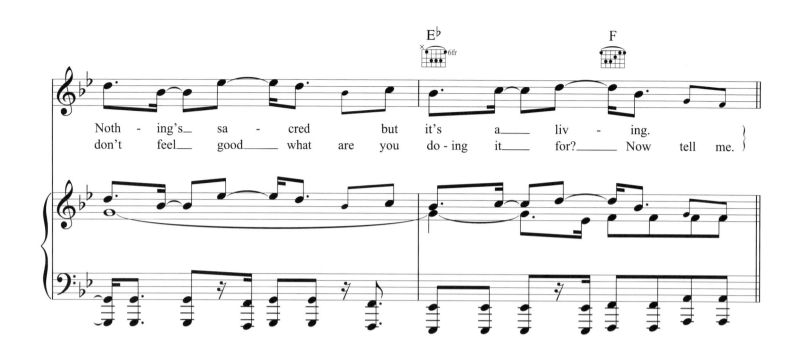

Noth - ing's__ sa - cred but it's a__ liv - ing.
don't feel__ good__ what are you do - ing it__ for?__ Now tell me.

Hey! Ho! Here she go. Ei - ther a lit - tle too high or a lit - tle too low. With no__

__ self es - teem and ver - ti - go 'cause she thinks she's made of can - dy.

Hey! Ho! Here she go. Ei - ther a lit - tle too loud or a lit - tle too close. With a

hur - ri - cane___ at the back of her throat she thinks she's made of can - dy.___

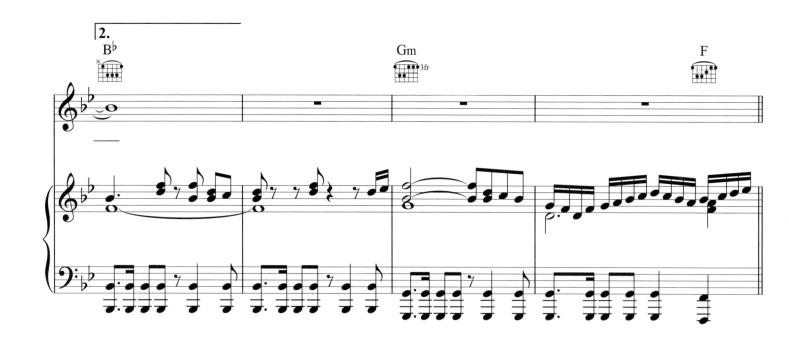

Li - ber - ate___ your sons and_ daugh-ters. The bush is___ high but in the

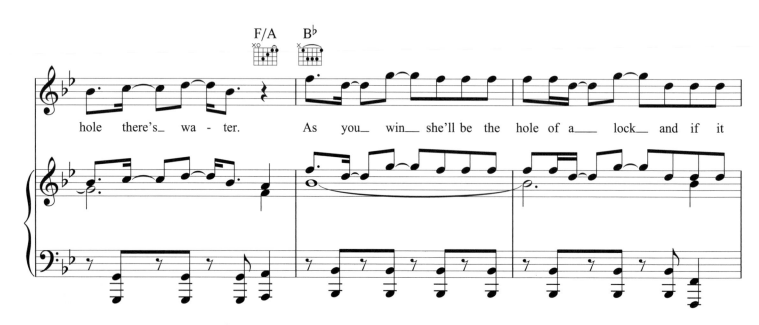

hole there's_ wa - ter. As you_ win_ she'll be the hole of a_ lock_ and if it

1, 3. Hey! Ho! Here she go. Ei-ther a lit-tle too high or a lit-tle too low. With no__
2, 4. Hey! Ho! Here she go. Ei-ther a lit-tle too loud or a lit-tle too close. With a

__ self es-teem and ver-ti-go ⎫ 'cause she thinks she's made of can-dy.
hur-ri-cane__ at the back of her throat ⎭

1-3.

4.

thinks she's made of can - dy._____

Half Of Me

Words & Music by Mikkel Eriksen, Tor Erik Hermansen,
Shahid Khan & Emeli Sandé

1. You saw me on a te-le-vi-sion, setting fire to all the build - ings.

Yeah, I guess you saw me steal - ing, but you've no i - dea what I've been need - ing.

Talk a - bout when we were child - ren, not the kind - a kid that you be - lieve in. You

kin-da songs that I been sing-ing_____ makes it seem as if I'm al-ways win-ning._ But you

saw me on a te-le-vi-sion,____ yeah, you saw me on a te-le-vi-sion._ But that's just the

half_ of it._ You saw the half of____ it.___

This is the life I___ live_____ and that's just the

half of_____ it._____ Oh,_____ you__ ___ know me, I'm the life of the par - ty. Beau-ti-ful peo - ple sur-round__ ___ me. Ev-'ry-bod-y fall-ing in love._____ Oh,_____ you__

know me, ev-'ry-bod-y knows that I'm cra - zy. Sticks and stones,___ they nev-er break___

me ___ and I'm the type that don't give a f***._____ And that's just the

half of_____ it.___ Yeah, you saw the half of_____ it.___
(2° vocal ad lib.)

He Ain't Heavy, He's My Brother

Words & Music by Bob Russell & Robert William Scott

strong,_____ strong e-nough to car - ry him._____

He ain't heav - y, he's my broth-er._____ So on we

go, his wel-fare__ is of my con-cern. No bur-den__ is__

he   to bear,   we'll get____ there._____   For I

know_____   he would_ not en - cum - ber_ me.

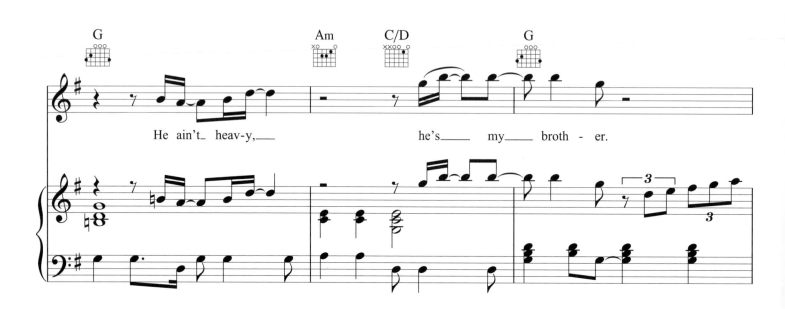

He ain't_ heav-y,____   he's___ my___ broth - er.

28

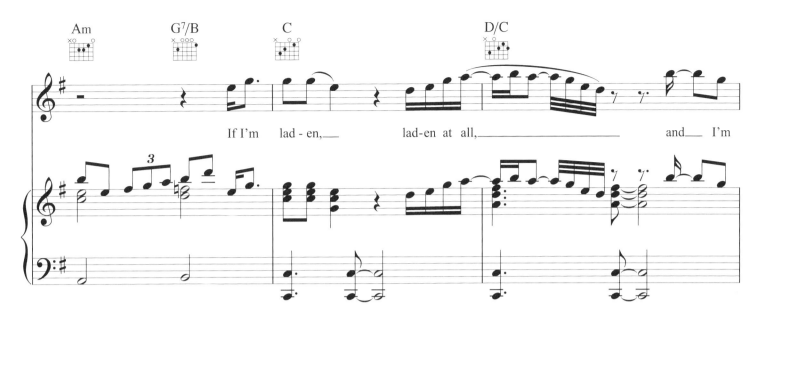

If I'm lad - en,___ lad-en at all,_____ and___ I'm

la - den___ with sad - ness that ev - 'ry - one's___ heart is - n't

filled___ with the glad - ness___ of___ love._____ for___ one an-

-oth - er. It's a long, long road

from which there__ is no re - turn, while we're on__ the__

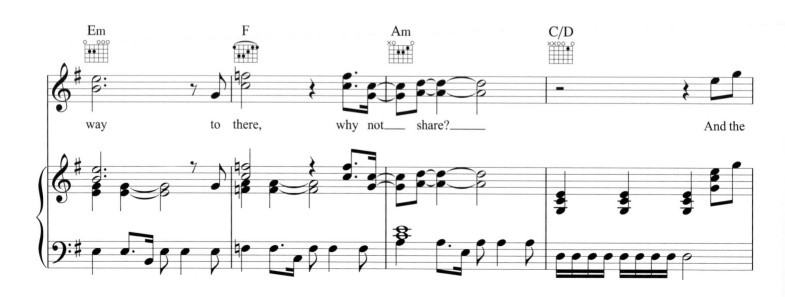

way to there, why not__ share?__ And the

load_____ it does-n't weigh me down at all.

'cause he ain't heav - y, he's my broth - er._____

He's my

Ho Hey

Words & Music by Jeremy Fraites & Wesley Schultz

love,   we need___ it now. Let's hope___   for some.

'Cause oh,___   we're bleed - ing out. I be-long with

you, you be-long with me you're my_ sweet - heart.___ I be-long with you, you be-long with me you're my_ sweet...

Ho!   Hey!   Ho!   Hey!

Impossible

Words & Music by Arnthor Birgisson & Ina Wroldsen

Little Things

Words & Music by Ed Sheeran & Fiona Bevan

Locked Out Of Heaven

Words & Music by Ari Levine, Philip Lawrence
& Peter Hernandez

takes me to pa - ra - dise. Yeah, your sex takes me to pa - ra - dise and it shows. Yeah,

yeah, yeah. 'Cause you make me feel like

I've been locked out of heav - en, for too

51

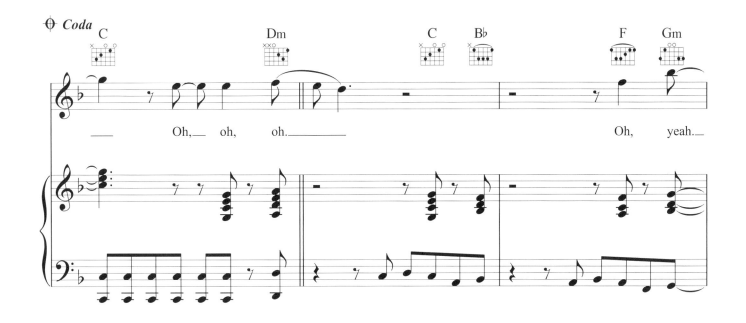

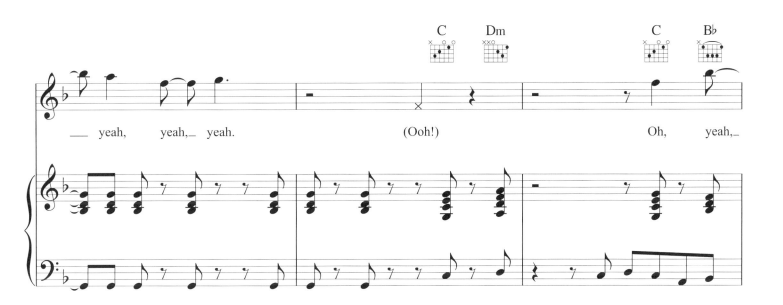

Lovebird

Words & Music by Lukasz Gottwald, Bonnie McKee
& Joshua Coleman

and that beau-ti-ful song bird.___ You used to call me your love-bird.

But the time went on,___ the wind has blown___ and I've grown.___

And I start-ed a feel-ing, that my wings have been bro-ken.

And I can't be-lieve___ that I would ev-er want___ to be___ set free,___

55

but I just can't___ stay,_____ so your love-bird's fly - ing a - way.___

Your love-bird's fly-ing a-way,___ 'cause my heart's been stuck in a cage.___ Got-ta sing___ my

song so pret-ty, dum dum did-dy. And I'll miss you ev - 'ry day___ but there's noth-ing left to say_

_____ Got-ta sing___ my song so pret-ty, dum dum did-dy. 2. I want the world at my feet

58

One More Night

Words & Music by Savan Kotecha, Adam Levine,
Martin Max & Johan Schuster

I stopped us-ing my head, us-ing my head, let it all go. Ooh._____ Got

you stuck on my bod - y, on my bod-y like a tat-too._____ And

now I'm feel-in' stu - pid, feel-in' stu - pid crawl-ing back to you._____ So I

cross my heart and I hope to die,_____ that I'll

on - ly stay with you one more night._____ And I

know I said it a mil - lion times_____ but I'll

on - ly stay with you one more night._____ 2. Try to tell you

Ooh, ooh ooh ooh ooh ooh ooh ooh._____ Yeah, ba - by give me

one more___ night. Ooh, ooh ooh ooh ooh ooh ooh ooh.___

1. ___ Yeah, ba-by give me one more___ night. ___

2. But

ba-by, there you go a-gain, there you go a-gain, mak-ing me love you. Yeah,

I stopped us-ing my head, us-ing my head, let it all go.___ Got

64

Skyfall

Words & Music by Paul Epworth & Adele Adkins

Troublemaker

Words & Music by Stephen Robson, Claude Kelly,
Olly Murs & Flo Rida

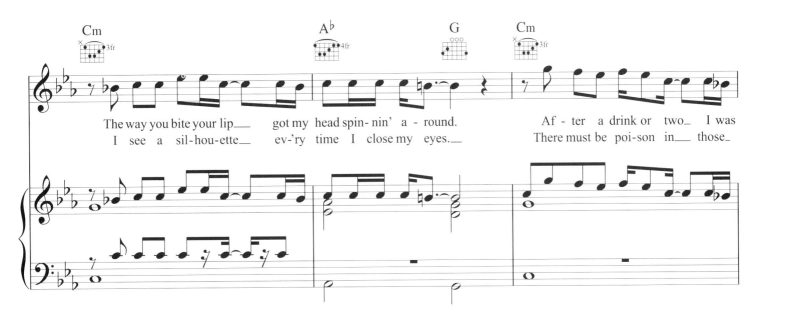

The way you bite your lip___ got my head spin-nin' a - round.
I see a sil-hou-ette___ ev-'ry time I close my eyes.___

Af - ter a drink or two___ I was
There must be poi-son in___ those_

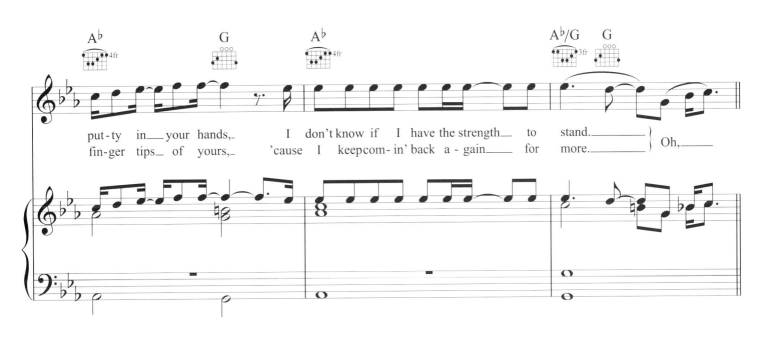

put-ty in___ your hands,_ I don't know if I have the strength___ to stand.___
fin-ger tips_ of yours,_ 'cause I keep com-in' back a - gain___ for more.___

Oh,___

trou-ble, trou-ble-mak-er, yeah, that's your mid-dle name._ Oh,___ I know you're no good but you're

stuck in my brain   and I wan-na know: Why   does it feel so good but hurt so__ bad?_   Oh,_____

my   mind keeps say - ing "Run   as   fast   as   you   can."__

I   say I'm done but then you pull me__ back.._   Oh,_____   I   swear you're giv-ing me a

pull me___ back.___ Oh,_____ I swear you're giv - ing me a

heart at - tack. Trou - ble - mak - er! May - be I'm___ in - sane 'cause

I keep do - ing the same___ damn thing. Think - ing one day we___ gon' change. But you

78

Bringing you the words and the music

All the latest music in print... rock & pop plus jazz, blues, country, classical and the best in West End show scores.

- Books to match your favourite CDs.

- Book-and-CD titles with high quality backing tracks for you to play along to. Now you can play guitar or piano with your favourite artist... or simply sing along!

- Audition songbooks with CD backing tracks for both male and female singers for all those with stars in their eyes.

- Can't read music? No problem, you can still play all the hits with our wide range of chord songbooks.

- Check out our range of instrumental tutorial titles, taking you from novice to expert in no time at all!

- Musical show scores include *The Phantom Of The Opera*, *Les Misérables*, *Mamma Mia* and many more hit productions.

- DVD master classes featuring the techniques of top artists.